Alynne
with Love from
Mother

Some favorite poems
from your childhood.

T5-AQA-578

Favorite Poems of Dorothy Aldis

About the Book

Of the many poems Dorothy Aldis wrote during her long career here are her own favorites. Although these poems have all been published over the last half century, just a few of them are still in print in other volumes. A few of these rhymes were slightly revised by Dorothy Aldis, even after first publication, but most of them remain as originally published.

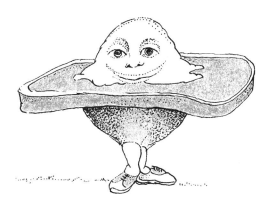

favorite poems of Dorothy Aldis

drawings by
Jack Lerman

G. P. Putnam's Sons • New York

Copyright © 1970 by Roy E. Porter

All rights reserved. Published simultaneously in the
Dominion of Canada by Longmans Canada Limited, Toronto.

Library of Congress Catalog Card Number: 75-110323

PRINTED IN THE UNITED STATES OF AMERICA
05209

Contents

Favorite Poems of Dorothy Aldis

The covers now are open wide,
So turn the page and step inside,
And you will find some children who
Are doing things you always do:
Playing games or getting dressed,
Hearing stories they like best,
Sitting at their cream of wheat
And being Bad, or Good, or Neat.
They'd like to have you stay with them
For a while and play with them —
Oh, please come in. For they are only
Picture children and feel lonely.

Radiator Lions

George lives in an apartment and
His mother will not let
Him keep a dog or polliwog
Or rabbit for a pet.

So he has Radiator Lions.
(The parlor is their zoo.)
They love to fight but never bite
Unless George tells them to.

But days when it is very cold
And George can't go outdoors,
His parlor pets will glower
And crouch upon all fours.

And roar most awful roarings.
The noise is very bad.
Up their noses water goeses —
That's what makes them mad.

But George loves Radiator Lions.
He's glad, although they're wild,
He hasn't dogs or polliwogs
Like any other child.

Hello, Day

Hello, windy, springtime day.
Everybody's feeling gay.
Clothes on the clothesline do a dance
Skirts and dresses. Shirts and pants.
Vines are waving. Treetops blow.
Flowers curtsy in a row.

But in summer, soft and gray,
You sometimes hold your breath, warm day.
Till suddenly comes the rush of rain
Soaking fields and woods again,
Sending us all indoors to play —
Still, hello, day.

And then the first time when our eyes
Know by an early morning light,
That all the world outdoors is white.
Trees and bushes bending low.
Not one footstep in the snow.

Oh, hello, day.

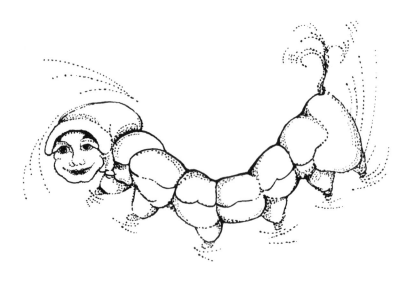

Inch-Worm

Little green worm,
Inch-worming, inch.
You can't hurt me
For you don't pinch.
You can't do
Anyone harm.
So take your walk
Up my arm.

In Early May

An unmown lawn
In early May
Is green and deep,
And children play
It's an ocean on
A windy day.
And any drifted
Leaf's a boat
With twigs for oars
Afloat, afloat.
And very gayly
All around
Without a breath
Without a sound
Dips a yellow
Butterfly,
And dandelion heads
Go bobbing by....

Hiding

I'm hiding, I'm hiding,
And no one knows where,
For all they can see is my
Toes and my hair.

And I just heard my father
Say to my mother,
"But, darling, he must be
Somewhere or other;

Have you looked in the inkwell?"
And Mother said, "Where?"
"In the inkwell," said Father. But
I was not there.

Then "Wait!" cried my mother.
"I think that I see
Him under the carpet." But
It was not me.

"Inside the mirror's
A pretty good place,"
Said Father and looked, but saw
Only his face.

"We've hunted," sighed Mother,
"As hard as we could,
And I am so afraid that we've
Lost him for good."

Then I laughed out aloud,
And I wiggled my toes,
And Father said, "Look, dear,
I wonder if those

Toes could be Benny's.
There are ten of them. See?"
And they were so surprised to find
Out it was me!

Flower Party

If flowers ever gave a party
This is what I'd wear:
Lady slippers on my foot,
Harebells in my hair.

On my hands two foxglove gloves.
A pink moss rose, my dress.
A sash? Would morning-glory vines
Tied behind
Be best?

And what for trimming underwear?
And ruffles near my face?
Why anyone would know I guess:
Queen Anne's lace.

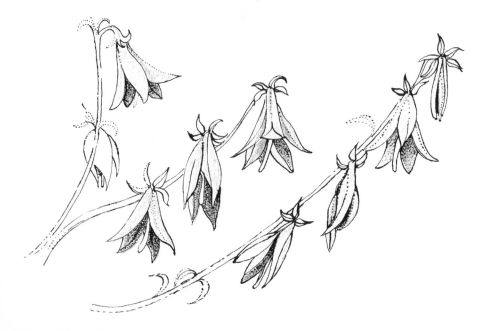

A Secret

On a quiet summer's night
How does he flash his little light?
Many people wonder this —
Doctors do and scientists.

Do you know
What makes him glow?

Uncle Timothy

Nice Uncle Timothy's never at home.
He's sometimes in Norway and sometimes in Rome.
He travels around with a big brown sack,
And we have to go kiss him when he gets back.

We like Uncle Timothy, but there's that nose — it
Snorts and shakes fiercely, whenever he blows it,
And on his face there are patches of prickles.
Wherever we kiss him, each prickle tickles.

Nice Uncle Timothy opens his sack
And gives us the playthings he has brought back —
Trolls from Norway and dollies from Rome —
So we *have* to go kiss him, when he gets home.

Ironing

The smell of ironing being done
Is pleasant to the nose —
It's not like flowers in the sun
Or new baked cookies laid in rows,
But just as fresh and warm a whiff
Rises on an ironing day
From little dresses, pressed and stiff,
Waiting to go out and play.

Some Thoughts

When people's clothes
    Are made with spots,
I jump around
    Between the dots.

When wallpaper
    Is vines and trees,
I lie in bed
    And climb on these,

And when in planes
    I sit so still,
I'm hopscotching
    From hill to hill.

21

Butterflies

Drifting lightly in the air
Small and bright and everywhere —
Yellow, orange, purple, blue.
Flocks of little white ones, too.
Fluttering up;
Then down again.
Sucking flowers,
Drinking rain.
Before they started all of this,
Each was in a chrysalis.
A furry caterpillar then
Waiting for the instant when
He could show us: "Look at me,
I'm not what I used to be,
For I have wings and can fly high;
Watch me be a butterfly!"

The Rain

The rain is raising prickles
In my little pool
And washing all the dirty worms
Pink and beautiful

And mussing up the dandelions'
Fuzzy yellow hairs
And making me come in the house
And go and play upstairs.

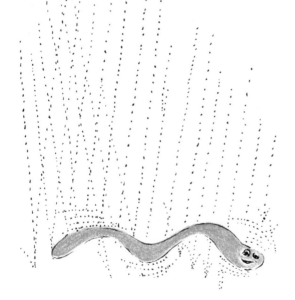

Lazy Day

Began to play
Croquet today.
Gave it up, though —
Walked away.
Wondered should
I climb a tree?
But got watching
A bumblebee.
Started this
And started that . . .
Thought I'd sit.
So I sat.

25

Feet

There are things
Feet know
That hands never will:
The exciting
Pounding feel
Of running down a hill;

The soft cool
Prickliness
When feet are bare
Walking in
The summer grass
To almost anywhere;

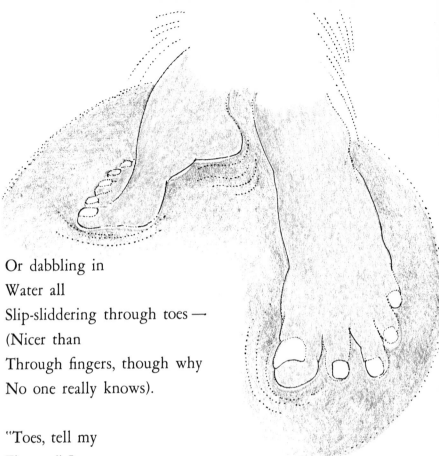

Or dabbling in
Water all
Slip-sliddering through toes —
(Nicer than
Through fingers, though why
No one really knows).

"Toes, tell my
Fingers," I
Said to them one day,
"Why it's such
Fun just to
Wiggle and play."

But toes just
Looked at me
Solemn and still.
Oh, there are things
Feet know
That hands *never will*.

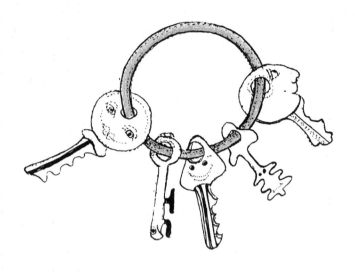

My Keys

I have a set of little keys.
They do not open any door.
That isn't what my keys are for.
My keys jingle, *my* keys shine.
I love my keys because they're mine.
I'll never want a set of keys,
Excepting these.

Leaf Crowns

When colored leaves are on the ground,
Pink, yellow, red,
Then I sit down and make a crown
And place it on my head.

Then I go running down the street
And sing a noisy song;
I feel the pounding of my feet
And pull the wind along.

Mary Ann's Luncheon

Here comes Mary Anne.
She has a clean face.
She tucks in her bib,
Climbs up in her place

And says she is ready
To eat right away.
But what about us —
Have *we* nothing to say:

For we are her luncheon,
yum yummy, yum yummy,
And we're all going down
to visit her tummy.

The Poached Egg says:
I'm a poached egg.
I sit on my toast
And wonder which fork prick
Will tickle the most.

And the Milk says:
I am the milk
In her own little cup,
And soon Mary Anne
Will drink me all up.

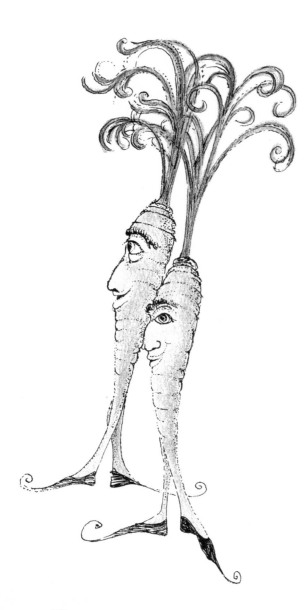

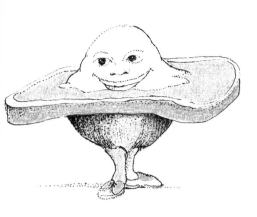

Oh, we are her luncheon,
yum yummy, yum, yummy,
And we're all going down
to visit her tummy.

Then the Egg speaks
again, very sadly:
Oh, what a fork prick!
Oh, what a thrust!
My beautiful yellow
Middle is bust.

And the Milk says:
I'm almost gone
Down her little red lane.
In a minute her cup
Will be empty again.

For we are her luncheon,
yum yummy, yum yummy.
And we're all going down
to visit her tummy.

And the Carrots say:
We are the carrots.
We like little girls,
And when we're inside them,
We grow rows of curls.

And the Custard says:
I am the custard,
Who makes a quick trip
Off the edge of her spoon
With a slide and a slip.

And the Carrots
speak cheerfully:
Just one more bite
Of us carrots to chew,
And then pretty soon
Mary Anne will be through.

And the Custard
sounds surprised:
It's certainly strange
The way I disappear:
I *was* in her saucer,
And now I am here.

Oh, we once were her luncheon,
yum yummy, yum yummy,
But now we are all dancing
round in her tummy.

Then good Mary Anne
Gets down from the table
And folds up her bib
As well as she's able.

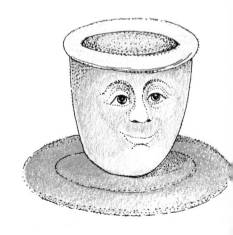

She walks very straight,
So as not to upset,
And she's glad that it isn't
Her suppertime yet.

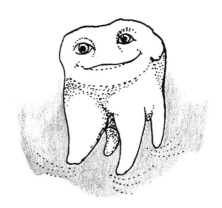

A Loss

A tooth that's chewed so faithfully,
Through many steaks and chops
And plates of peas and carrots, why,
It's horrid when he stops.

He's wobbling rather badly and
Is wiggly to the touch —
Oh, when he's gone, I will not like
Another tooth as much!

Spring Promise

How can you know when I will come?
By the wild geranium.
One morning they will open wide
And like a lovely purple tide
Flood the woods and fields and spill
Across the road and down the hill.
And then I will, and then I will!

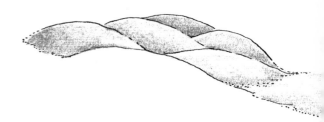

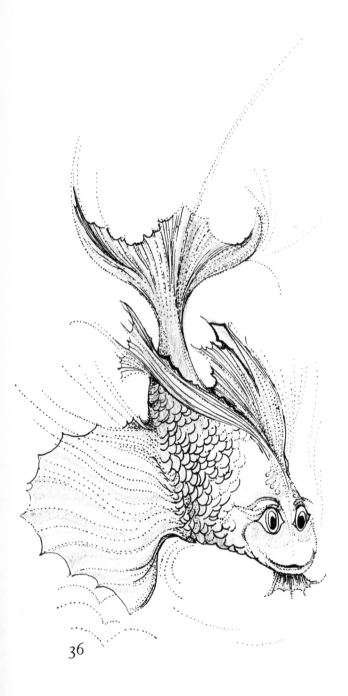

The Goldfish

My darling little goldfish
Hasn't any toes;
He swims around without a sound
And bumps his hungry nose.

He can't get out to play with me,
Nor I get in to him,
Although I say: "Come out and play,"
And he — "Come in and swim."

Today

Today. Beginning of the spring:
One little snowdrop blossoming.

Everything else is brown and bare
Till all of a sudden through the air,
Making us lift our faces: snow.
The fall is peaceful, soft and slow —

One little snowdrop on the ground,
Millions and trillions coming down.

I Am

I am a bridge
From one bed to another;
I am a whale
With frightened fish to chase;
I am a boat
Sailing round my mother —

How can I be a little boy
And wash my hands and face?

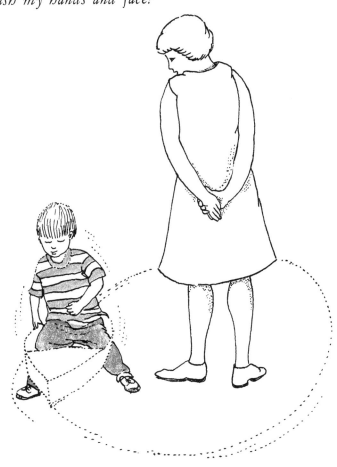

Quite Busy

These are some games I like to play:
When shoes lie around, I take them away.

When drawers are open, I put the shoes in —
They like to be where they've never been.

When papers are left on a desk or chair,
I move them quickly, away from there.

When I find candles, some ink or soap,
I taste them with the fondest hope.

There are a great many things to do —
Things to uncover and cover up, too.

And things that are sitting high up on a shelf
I try very hard to pull down on myself.

Dragons and Lions

Snap-Dragons and Dande-Lions
Are not so very wild —
I never yet saw one forget
And try to hurt a child.

A Dande-Lion never ROARS,
Not even once, for fun;
Nor waves his tail with angry wail —
Because he hasn't one!

A Snap-Dragon will never snap
No matter how he feels,
Not even to try to catch a fly
To brighten up his meals.

43

Friends

Children who are friends do not
Always see each other;
If it rains or they are bad,
They stay home with their mother.

But twice a day and every day,
No matter what the weather,
Little toothbrushes and teeth
HAVE to play together.

Choosing

It must be dull to be the street
And just see feet and feet and feet.
It must be dull to be the sky!
But of the two I think that I
Would rather be a slice of sky
Than a sidewalk or a street:
Stars when they go skipping by
Must be prettier than feet.

After Supper

Let's not pretend we're anywhere;
Let's simply sit here in this chair.

I don't want to play that we
Are sailors sailing on the sea,
Or pirates in a large, dark cave,
Or even lions being brave.

I'm feeling very nice and near.
Let's just be here.

In the Morning

Our father always shaves his face
Excepting in the bristles' place;

When he's walking down the stairs
He's sometimes mice and sometimes bears;

At breakfast time he eats two eggs
And holds his napkin on his legs,

And then he reaches up so high
We stand on chairs to say good-bye.

Good Children

Children who are brave and good
Always do the things they should.

Even when it happens to
Be something they don't want to do.

And every child, if he has hair,
Climbs into the barber's chair!

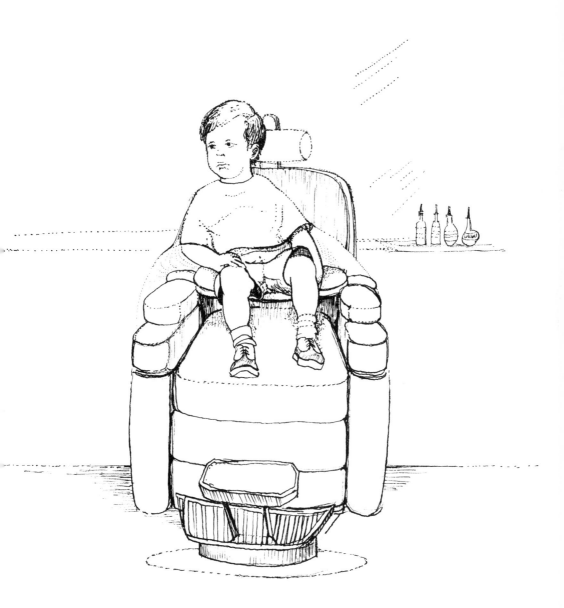

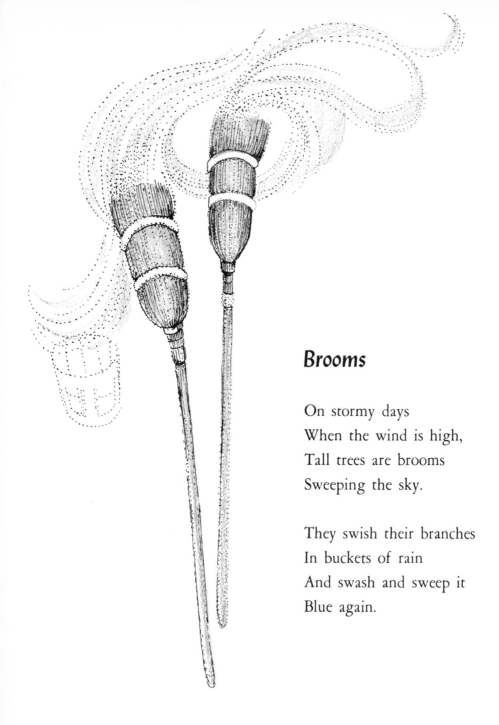

Brooms

On stormy days
When the wind is high,
Tall trees are brooms
Sweeping the sky.

They swish their branches
In buckets of rain
And swash and sweep it
Blue again.

Gayest of All

Spring noises: try to
Count how many —
Organs grinding
For a penny.
Balloon men blowing
Up the street.
Peddlers crying
Things to eat.
Shower spatters,
Skaters, skooters,
Baseball batters,
Marble shooters.
But gayest of all
The treetop song
Of robins, robins
All day long.

My Shoelace

My shoelace has a pleasant time
　　With nothing much to do.
Every morning it climbs up —
　　In evenings, down my shoe.
But nearly always I am there
　　Just to help it to.

The Nice Old Couple

When walking, they waddle, a little bit
Like friendly ducks in the rain;
She holds the umbrella, twirling it,
And he points at things with his cane.

He laughs when she says something, offers his arm,
As he leads her through the dripping weather.
They like it out in the April storm
Being cozy and old together.

Under the Sprinkler

Under the sprinkler
A whir and a chatter —
Birds in the garden
Enjoying a spatter;
Moistening a beak
Or preening a feather,
They're never surprised
At a quick change in weather.
Although it is August,
An elm tree away
They chirrup: "Not here,
Here-it's-May, here-it's-May."

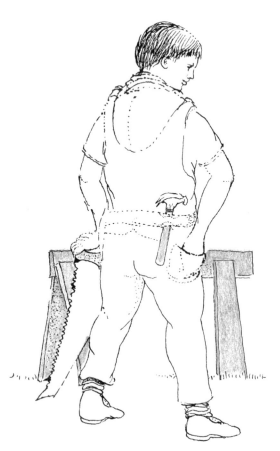

56

Carpenters and Gardeners

Carpenters and gardeners
Are always glad to talk.
Laying down a handsaw
Or leaning on a hoe,
They'll forget the cupboard shelf
Or the weedy stalk
And tell you, very patiently,
Anything they know.

Grown-Up

I'm growing up, my mother says —
Today she said I'd grown;
The reason why is this: Now I
Can do things all alone.

And though I'm glad that I don't need
Someone to brush my hair
Or wash my hands and face and button
Buttons everywhere.

Although I'm very glad indeed
To help myself instead,
I hope that I won't have to try
TO TUCK MYSELF IN BED!

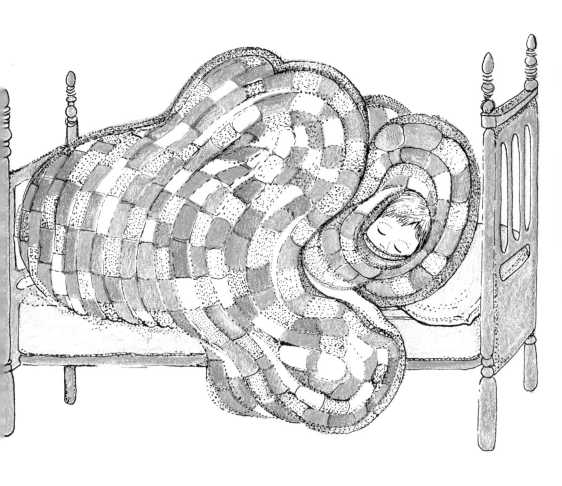

The Ice Had All Melted

The ice had all melted and I went to look
To see what was stirring in our little brook:
Black sticks. Autumn grasses. Three acorns afloat.
A curled-up brown leaf sailing by like a boat.

I lowered my face, then shielded my eyes
To peer deeper down — and what a surprise:
A flash of bright minnows, alive as could be,
Saw I was alive and were frightened of me!

Certainly Somebody

Certainly somebody must have been out
With buckets of dandelions last night;
Somebody must have tossed them about
In meadows, on roadsides, left and right —
Just look at them scattered and spattered around
Like big yellow pennies all over the ground!

Before Things Happen

I like it before
Things happen quite —
A bird with his wings
Just lifted for flight;
Fields on the brink
Of blossoming clover;
A green wall of water
About to curl over.
Just that second, just that wink
Before you can say,
"See the wave. Oh, how pink.
Watch the bird fly away."

Index of First Lines

The Author

DOROTHY ALDIS never lost her affinity for the things that appeal to children, such as creatures (especially the crawling varieties), imaginative tales, and innocent intrigue. After her graduation from Smith College, she used an assumed name to land a job on the Chicago *Tribune*. She was writer of the *Tribune*'s cat and dog department and lonely hearts column before the editor, her father, knew she was a member of the *Tribune* staff. Before she died in 1966, Dorothy Aldis' verse appeared in several major magazines and in twenty-seven books for children. Five of the twenty-seven were published by Putnam and are still available; they are: *All Together, Cindy, Dumb Stupid David, Is Anybody Hungry?,* and *Quick as a Wink.*